Chords

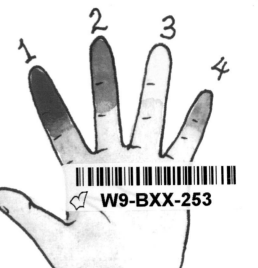

G
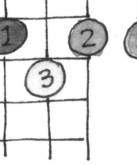

A
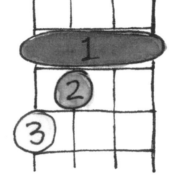

B

G7
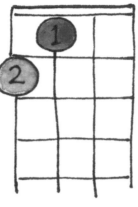

A7
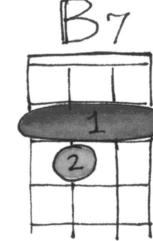

B7

Gm
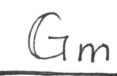
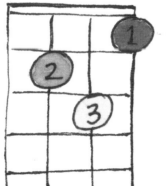

Am
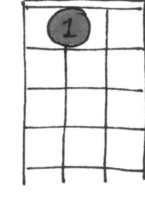

Bm
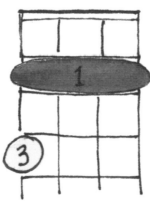

For Calen and Tyler
Dr. C & J.C.

For Lindsey, Zane and Aiden
A.K.

Banana Patch Press
www.BananaPatchPress.com

Text Copyright ©2012 Dr. Carolan & Auntie Kealoha
Illustrations Copyright ©2012 Joanna Carolan
All rights reserved

Library of Congress Control Number: 2011916539
ISBN: 978-0-9800063-1-5

Printed in Hong Kong

The Magic 'Ukulele

Dr. Carolan
&
Auntie Kealoha

Illustrated by
Joanna Carolan

Audio CD:
Roy Sakuma
Ken Emerson

Some 'ukuleles are magic.
Did you know?

A magic 'ukulele can take you
anywhere you want to go.

Just pluck on its strings, and think about
wonderful places and things.

Play a few chords,
hit the right note,
and you can be on a boat.

Play a few more,
and hold on to your pants!
You can be anywhere,
even in Paris, France.

You can be in a little French café,
with an artist wearing a purple beret,
watching a French poodle cabaret.

Then play another chord and think, "olé!"
And you can be off and on your way.

You can go to southern Spain,
no need for a car or train!

Would you like to visit Tokyo?
Pluck a string and change your tempo.

Play some more and hold onto your hat,
you can be anywhere in two seconds flat!

Waltz
in Vienna before noon.

Tango
by a blue lagoon.

Two-step
into a Texas saloon.

Boogie
in Jamaica
to a reggae tune.

Dance with a dragon
in Kowloon.

Playing the 'ukulele is lots of fun.
But how can you tell if your 'ukulele
is a magic one?

Is your 'ukulele old or new?
Is your 'ukulele red, yellow, pink or blue?

Does it need to be made from mahogany?
Should it be made of koa, rosewood,
maple, spruce or ebony?

No, it is not the color that does the trick.
No, no! It is not the type of wood
that makes it magic!

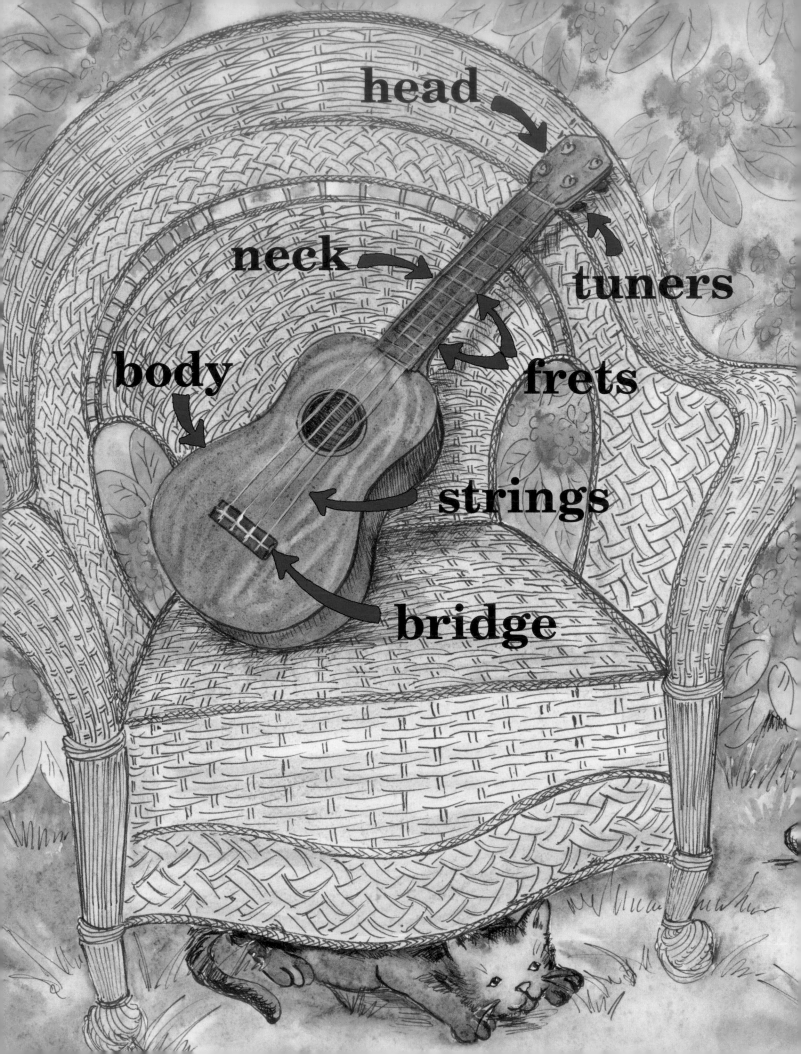

Is the magic some part of its anatomy?
Is it the head, the neck, or the body?

Is it the bridge, frets, tuners or strings?
No, no, no. It is not any of these things!

So, how can you tell
if your 'ukulele is a magic one?
How can you find out? How is it done?

First tune your 'ukulele:
G,
C,
E,
A, please.

It's easy to remember,
just think:
My
Dog
Has
Fleas.

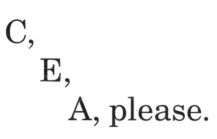

There is only one way,
to get a magic 'ukulele,
right now,
starting
today:
You must play,
and play,
and play,
and
play.

Play when
you are happy
and glad.

Play when you are
blue and sad.

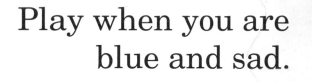

Play when you are angry or mad.

Play an old song, or play something new.
Play when you are bored and have
nothing else to do.

Play when it is raining.
Play in the sunshine.

Play when you are
waiting in a long line.

Play very softly.
Play very loud.

Play alone or with a crowd.

Never give up and then one day,
you'll find yourself transported away.

Your fingers will find every right note.
You won't need an airplane or a boat.

You just wish for a tropical breeze
and find yourself sitting
under palm trees.

Your magic 'ukulele will take you
wherever you want to be,
like the white, sandy
beaches of Waikiki.

Strum to the North Shore and catch a wave,
Surf at Pipeline, if you are brave.

Want to see hot lava flow?
Finger pick your way
to Kilauea volcano!

If that fast picking
makes you sweat,
do not worry,
do not fret...

Change your rhythm, feel the ocean spray,
and jump right into Hanauma Bay!
See the humuhumu-nukunuku-ā-pua'a
go swimming by, and then...

... faster than a nene can fly,
feel the mists of Fern Grotto
on beautiful Kaua'i.

Float on tiny bubbles
up to the moon.
See the stars up close and
play them a tune.

Twinkle, twinkle little star
how I wonder what you are.

When you are tired and ready for bed,
put down your magic 'ukulele
and rest your head.

Dream of rhythms fast and slow.
Dream of notes high and low.
Dream of where you want to go.
Dream somewhere over the rainbow.

Dream about
places near or far away.
You can go there
another day.
Just pick up your
magic 'ukulele,
and play,
and play,
and play…

The Magic 'Ukulele Song
Words by Dr. Carolan
Play to the tune of *Twinkle, Twinkle Little Star*

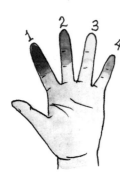

C

F

G7

(C)   (F)   (C)
'Ukulele, little guitar,

(G7)   (C)   (G7)   (C)
Came to Hawai'i from a far!

(C)   (G7)   (C)   (G7)
It has magic, I'll tell you why,

(C)   (G7)   (C)   (G7)
As the stars spin in the sky!

(C)   (F)   (C)
'Ukulele, little guitar,

(G7)   (C)   (G7)   (C)
You are magic, yes, you are!

Strumming, strumming every day,
Your 'ukulele is fun to play!
Pluck on each and every string,
Make your 'ukulele sing!
Strumming, strumming on its strings,
Dream of wonderful places and things!

To go anywhere near or far,
You don't need a train and you don't
need a car!
Feel the rhythm, feel the beat,
Your 'ukulele is sounding sweet!
Practice, practice every day,
Your 'ukulele will sweep you away!

Low notes, high notes, here we go,
Strumming fast or strumming slow!
You are learning very quick,
You make the 'ukulele magic!
Strumming, strumming every day,
Your 'ukulele is fun to play!

Strumming, strumming every day,
Magic 'ukulele, hip, hip hooray!

Jumping Flea Song
Words by Dr. Carolan
Play to the tune of *London Bridge is Falling Down*

A

E7

(A)
Oh, I love my jumping flea,

(E7)   (A)
Jumping flea, jumping flea.

(A)
Yes, I love my jumping flea,

(E7)   (A)
My 'ukulele!

Oh, my jumping flea loves me,
Flea loves me, flea loves me.
Yes, my jumping flea loves me,
My 'ukulele!

Play it when I'm blue and sad,
Blue and sad, blue and sad.
Play it when I'm blue and sad,
My 'ukulele!

'Cause it makes me happy and glad,
Happy and glad, happy and glad.
'Cause it makes me happy and glad,
My 'ukulele!

Oh, I love my jumping flea,
Jumping flea, jumping flea.
Yes, I love my jumping flea,
My 'ukulele!

'Ukulele Fun Facts!

 The first 'ukulele was brought to Hawai'i in 1879 by Portuguese immigrants from island of Madeira. They sailed to Hawai'i on a ship named *Ravenscrag*.

 In Portugal, the 'ukulele was called a *barguinha* before it came to Hawai'i.

 The Portuguese *barguinha* has four strings like the 'ukulele, but it's tuning is different.

 In the early days, the 'ukulele was sometimes called a "taro patch fiddle" because it was played by the workers in the taro fields.

 'Ukulele means "jumping flea" in Hawaiian, and refers to the way a player's fingers jump along the strings (*uku* – flea, *lele* – jump or hop).

 Hawaiian words often have several meanings. 'Ukulele can also be translated as "the gift that came here" (*uku* – gift or reward, and *lele* – to come). Queen Lili'uokalani is said to have preferred this translation for 'ukulele over "jumping flea".

 The Hawaiian monarchy championed the 'ukulele and helped to make it popular in Hawai'i and around the world. King Kalākaua, Queen Emma, Queen Lili'uokalani and Princess Likelike were said to be accomplished 'ukulele players.

 The 'ukulele gained worldwide exposure at the 1915 Panama-Pacific International Exposition in San Francisco, attended by 17 million people. 'Ukulele music was featured at the Hawaiian Pavilion and the craze for the 'ukulele and Hawaiian music soon swept the country.

 A Guinness World Record for the largest 'ukulele ensemble was set in Sweden on August 20, 2011 by 1547 fun-loving 'ukulele players.

About the READ ALONG CD:

Narrated by Roy Sakuma
'Ukulele and Slack Key Guitar by Ken Emerson
'Ukulele Lullaby composed by Ken Emerson
Vocals by Millicent Cummings and Roy Sakuma's 'Ukulele Students:
Kolby Agpaoa, Madison Garcia, Joelle Lee, Brandon Pave, Nelly Toyama-Baduria

Executive Producer Banana Patch Press
Producer Ron Pendragon
Sound Design, Recorded, Mixed & Mastered by
Ron Pendragon, Kaua'i, Hawai'i
www.FatTuesdayRecords.com

ROY SAKUMA

Roy Sakuma is recognized as Hawaii's foremost 'ukulele teacher and proponent of the instrument. He and his wife Kathy have four 'ukulele schools on O'ahu. Innovative, inspirational, warm and funny, Roy's unique method of instruction makes learning fast and – most of all – fun. Roy founded the annual 'Ukulele Festival in 1971, which has grown into the largest 'ukulele festival of its kind in the world. www.RoySakuma.net

KEN EMERSON

Ken Emerson began his musical career at age 7 playing the 'ukulele. He has been entertaining listeners around the world with his unique style for over 30 years. Recipient of the prestigious "Kahili" Award for perpetuating Hawaiian culture, Ken is also a contributing artist and composer on the first "Best Hawaiian Music Album" to win a GRAMMY® Award in 2006.

Auntie Kealoha, Dr. Carolan and Joanna Carolan

DR. CAROLAN was born in Melbourne, Australia. He moved to Hawai'i in 1977. He has been a pediatrician in private practice on the island of Kaua'i, Hawai'i since 1979. *The Magic 'Ukulele* is his eighth children's book.

JOANNA CAROLAN was born in San Francisco, California. Her grandparents moved to Kaua'i in 1967; she spent part of her teenage years living with them in Wailua. She is an artist and owner of Banana Patch Studio & Gallery on the island of Kaua'i.

AUNTIE KEALOHA aka Amy Hammond, is the president of Special Events Hawaii. She was born in Columbus, Ohio and graduated from the University of Hawai'i with an Honors degree in Communications. She is the author of the children's book *The Magic Sandman,* which was featured in *Chicken Soup from the Soul of Hawai'i.* www.TheMagicSandman.com

Other Dr. Carolan books available from Banana Patch Press:

> *Ten Days in Hawaii, A Counting Book*
> *B is for Beach, An Alphabet Book*
> *Where Are My Slippers? A Book of Colors*
> *Goodnight Hawaiian Moon*
> *Old Makana Had a Taro Farm*
> *This is My Piko*
> *A President From Hawai'i*

For more information visit:
www.BananaPatchPress.com

'Ukulele

C	D	E	F
	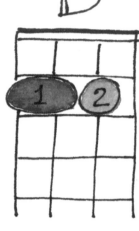	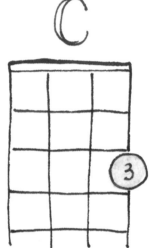	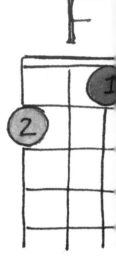

C7	D7	E7	F7
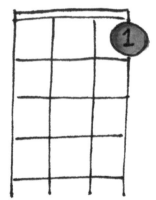		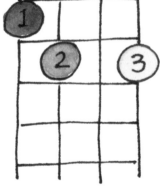	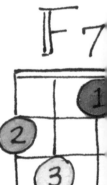

Cm	Dm	Em	Fm
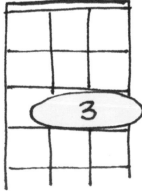	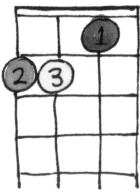	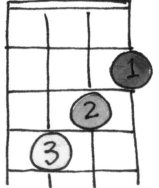